The story of David and Goliath

Retold by Susan Dickinson
Illustrated by Sally Holmes

Collins Colour Cubs

The Israelites and the Philistines were at war. The Israelite army of King Saul was camped on one hillside above a valley and

the Philistine army was camped on the
opposite hillside. The two armies faced
each other and prepared for battle.

In the Philistine army there was an enormous giant called Goliath. Goliath was so huge and so fierce that all the Israelites were afraid of him.

Every day Goliath strode down into the valley. Then he roared a challenge over to the Israelites: "Hey, you slaves of Saul! Choose a man to come and fight me! If he kills me we will be your slaves, but if I kill him you will be our slaves. I dare you. Choose someone to fight me." But nobody was brave enough.

There were three brothers in the Israelite army. Their young brother, David, had stayed at home with their father to look after the sheep.

One evening, David's father said to him:
"I want you to go to your brothers to see
how they are getting on. Take this food for
them and come back to me as soon as you
can." David travelled all night.

When he arrived at the camp the next morning he heard the soldiers saying that they were going to fight the Philistines that very day. David ran to look for his brothers.

He found them at last and was giving them their father's message, when Goliath appeared on the cliff across the valley and roared his challenge to the Israelites. "Is no one brave enough to fight me? Come and fight, you rabble!"

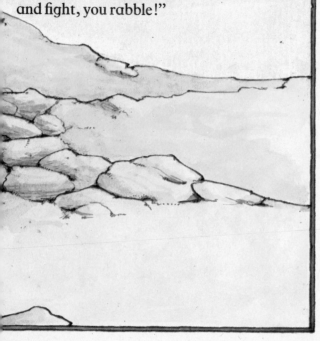

Some Israelite soldiers were filling their water pots in the stream. When they heard Goliath's shout, they ran back to their friends as fast as they could.

David saw this, and he asked: "Who has been chosen to fight this boastful fellow? And what is the reward for killing him?" There was no reply. "Well, somebody must kill him," David said. "I'll do it myself."

When he heard of this, King Saul sent for David. "You must not put your life at risk. You are only a young boy, and Goliath would certainly kill you," said the King.

But David insisted. So Saul offered him his own armour. David tried it on, but it was far too large for him. "I'm much happier in my own clothes," he said.

He took all the armour off, picked up his shepherd's crook, and the catapult he used for slinging stones at lions and bears that attacked his sheep, and set off down the hill.

At the stream, David picked up five pebbles and put them in his bag. Then he crossed the stream to meet Goliath.

When Goliath saw David coming, he shouted, "Do you think I'm frightened of a puny little fellow like you? Come on, come and be killed, and I'll give your body to the birds and animals to eat!"

David took no notice. He put his hand in his bag, took out a pebble, fitted it into his catapult and slung it at Goliath. It hit Goliath on the forehead and the giant fell to the ground, dead.

At the sight of Goliath lying dead on the ground the Israelites gave a great shout of joy, and rushed down the hillside to David. The Philistines, terrified, took to their heels and ran.